# Frankie

## the walk 'n roll dog

# Frankie
## the walk 'n roll dog

by barbara gail techel
illustrations by victoria kay lieffring

joyful paw prints

wisconsin

Illustrations by Victoria Kay Lieffring
Frankie's wheelchair manufactured by Eddie's Wheels, Shelburne Falls, MA
Website: www.eddieswheels.com

ISBN-10: 0-9800052-0-5
ISBN-13: 978-0-9800052-0-2

Summary: A tale of a dachshund whose life starts out just like any other dog, but at the age of six becomes paralyzed from a spinal injury. A wheelchair is custom made for her and she puts her best paw forward spreading the message of hope with everyone she meets. Appeal is to all children; teaches overcoming challenges and also compassion for the handicapped.

Printed in the United States

Published by Joyful Paw Prints, Elkhart Lake, WI 53020
Website: www.joyfulpaws.com Email: joyfulpaws@yahoo.com

joyful paw prints

dedicated to frankie, my little sweetheart.
you are my sunshine who showed me hope and
faith when mine was truly tested.

# Introduction

Easter Sunday 2006, my husband John and I were on vacation in Florida when our sweet dog Frankie's life changed forever. We felt so helpless so many miles away and our hearts felt like they would break in two. We were scared we might never see Frankie again.

The year that followed was filled with ups and downs, tears, laughter, love, determination and, most of all, hope.

Sometimes life does not go as planned. When this happens, we may feel lost, scared and confused. But if we open our minds to what lies ahead, we'll be pleasantly surprised.

As you can see by the picture on the cover, Frankie walks with the help of tires. Her life didn't start out that way. She was a regular dog who walked on all four legs. So, this is Frankie's life story, told by Frankie herself, through me, her loving, human mom.

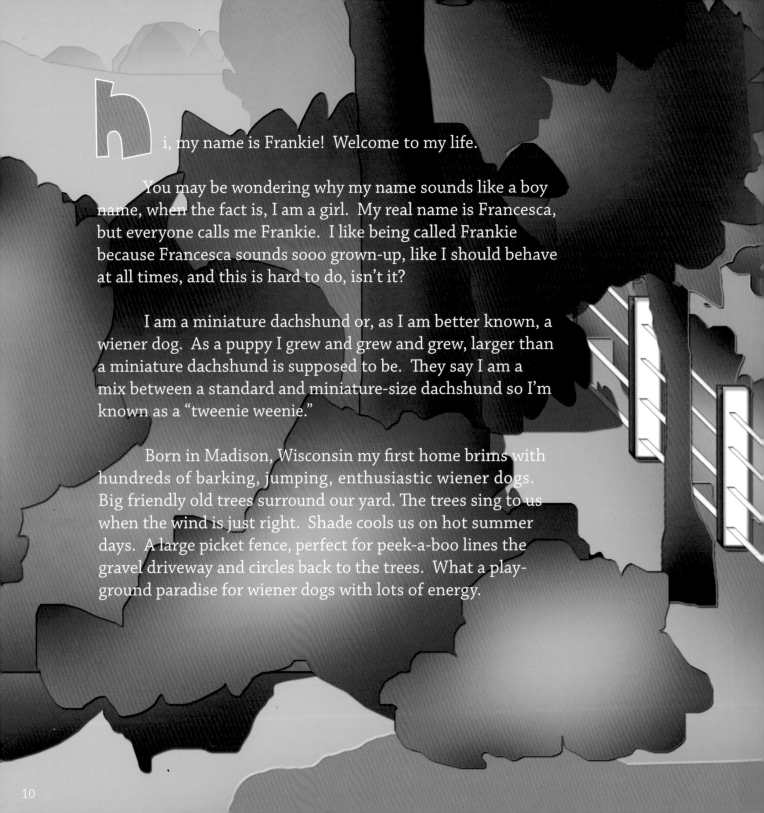

hi, my name is Frankie! Welcome to my life.

You may be wondering why my name sounds like a boy name, when the fact is, I am a girl. My real name is Francesca, but everyone calls me Frankie. I like being called Frankie because Francesca sounds sooo grown-up, like I should behave at all times, and this is hard to do, isn't it?

I am a miniature dachshund or, as I am better known, a wiener dog. As a puppy I grew and grew and grew, larger than a miniature dachshund is supposed to be. They say I am a mix between a standard and miniature-size dachshund so I'm known as a "tweenie weenie."

Born in Madison, Wisconsin my first home brims with hundreds of barking, jumping, enthusiastic wiener dogs. Big friendly old trees surround our yard. The trees sing to us when the wind is just right. Shade cools us on hot summer days. A large picket fence, perfect for peek-a-boo lines the gravel driveway and circles back to the trees. What a play-ground paradise for wiener dogs with lots of energy.

Days somersault by and I am the last pup of the litter to find a new home. I worry that no one wants me.... but then I see her... my new mom.

I am three months old and a petite blonde lady named Barb is watching me. I am happy. My teeth sparkle clean and I smile, lighting up the sky and my silky hair shines brightly. I wonder, is she the one?

I promenade down the gravel driveway to greet Barb by putting my best paw forward, walking with my head held high, showing off my spunky personality. I want to win this kind lady over with my irresistible good looks and charm.

When Barb sees me, big tears of joy roll down her cheeks. I flash my fawn-like eyes right into hers. It is love at first sight. She picks me up and cuddles me in her arms. It is the happiest feeling in the world and I feel right at home in Mom's safe hug.

I pace back and forth because the paperwork takes forever to complete. Once the dotted line is signed, I am lovingly placed in a pink kennel in the back seat of the car. I get comfortable among the soft blankets and quietly settle in for the two- hour ride to my new home. My heart is filled with happiness.

When we arrive at my new home, Mom lets me out of my kennel and I take a deep breath of fresh air. Home is an olive green cottage in the quaint village of Elkhart Lake. My mom places me on the grass but my legs are so short, you can barely see them in the long grass. My new dad, John, smiles and says, "Your legs must be on backorder!" Cassie, my new dog sister, is a tall chocolate lab, and she greets me with a sniff.

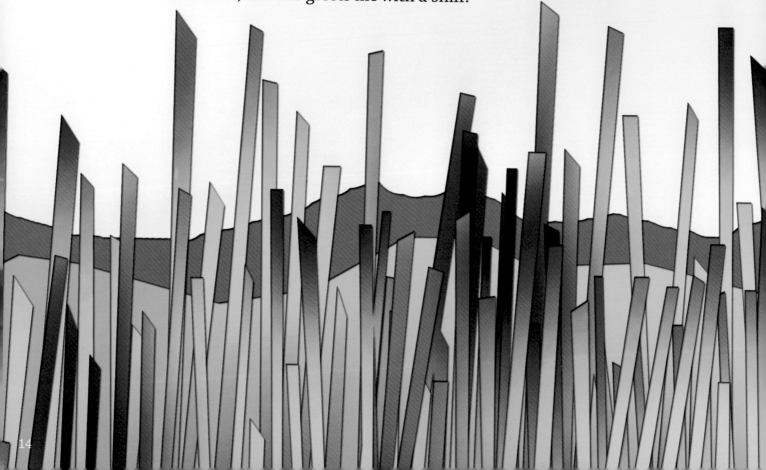

Mom carries me everywhere, tucked safely and securely in her right arm.  She i
afraid someone's going to step on me.  The first six months I am the size of a guinea p
Believe me, if someone steps on me, I'd let out a big SQUEAK!

At night, I sleep in a small, cozy, cushiony bed.  I nestle into warm fuzzy blanke
My bed sits on a chair next to Mom's side of the bed, so I am not scared.  The first nig
I cry.  I miss my wiener dog sisters and brothers and hope they have found wonderful
homes too.  The second night, I fall asleep within minutes.  I know everything is goin
to be fine because my new family loves me.

In the morning, I coo softly to wake Mom and Dad.  They stretch and yawn whe
they hear me.  My mom says, "Listen, John, Frankie is singing sweetly to us, just like

Learning how to go to the bathroom is a big ordeal for me. I cannot get the hang of going outside on the lawn. I prefer the warm house and the kitchen floor. After nine long months, Mom sternly shakes her finger at me and says, "Frankie, my patience has run out." I can see by the look in her eyes that she is upset. I better get the hang of

When summer comes, Mom gets out her shiny red bicycle. A special wicker basket rests on the front handle bars. This is for me to ride in. Before we ride, she dresses me in my pink paisley bandana and doggie sunglasses. We ride downtown to the Farmer's Market. I like to perch my two front paws on the edge of the basket. When the wind is just right, my ears glide out to the sides. I feel as if I can fly!

We near the market and hear people gleefully shout, "Look at the dog in the basket!" I love the attention and am very good at hamming it up. I bark and bark and bark! It's my way of letting them know I will be with them soon. We park our bike, begin to shop the market and visit with everyone.

I hustle along at the end of my blue leash with Mom as we make our way through the busy market. Delightful smells of baked goods and flowers waft through my nostrils. My tongue laps up any doughnut crumbs I find and I quickly snorkel them down. Yum, yum, yummy!

Kids love me! "Look at the wiener dog! Mom, can I pet the dog?" They cautiously come closer, asking permission to pet me. I love the soft sweet strokes of little kids and their kindnesses toward me. Their eyes light up with smiles stretching from ear to ear.

As we stroll among the tented canopies, we make our way to our favorite vendor, Jodee. She sells homemade dog treats that are baked fresh each week. Her dogs are Olive and Baci. They are toy fox terriers. Olive sits in a pink and black plaid pouch which hangs around her mom's neck, while Baci is held tight in her mom's arms. If it is a hot day, Olive shares her water with me. My mom and Jodee share dog stories while Olive, Baci and I close our eyes and soak up the warm sun.

I know it is time to go home when the back basket on our bike is full of goodies like strawberry jelly, homemade baked bread, colorful flowers, delicious vegetables and yummy doggie treats. Back into my basket I go for the slow ride home. Shopping wears a little dog out and I am tired. I rest my head on the side of the basket and half close my eyes. I let the sound of the birds sing me to sleep as Mom pedals us back home.

Once we are home, I get a bowl of cool water to quench my thirst. Then it is time for a nap. My favorite place to snooze is in the front of our house on the green lush lawn. The sun bakes into my fur and warms me inside-out. Before I know it, I am lulled into dreamland where I chase squirrels up trees and eat all the treats I want.

The summer flies by lickity-split. Before I know it, the leaves turn colors of popsicle orange, licorice red and yo-yo yellow. The earth changes around me and my dog sister, Cassie, gets sick with cancer. My mom, dad and I enjoy the time we have left with her. During the long, cold winter months, we snuggle close together. In spring, we bound outside to sniff the fresh new smells of the season. The flowers are in full bloom when Cassie dies. Mom and Dad cry. I sit in Mom's lap and cry too. We miss her so much!

One week before Christmas, Mom and Dad surprise me with a puppy sister, Kylie. She is a yellow Labrador. I love to press my warm body up against hers as we lay next to each other on my dancing kitty pillow. We keep each other warm and our snoring wakes up Mom and Dad during the night. As she grows, Kylie enjoys using me as a pillow and rests her head on my body. I do not mind being loved by her.

Spring is in the air once again because I see robins eating worms and the grass wets my paws. Mom and Dad tell Kylie and me they are going on vacation to a hot, tropical place called Florida. They take us to doggie daycare where I have stayed in the past. On the ride there, Mom says, "Before you know it, Frankie, we'll be back to pick you up!" I wag my tail happily.

We arrive and are placed in separate side-by-side cages. Kylie plays rough and pounces like a puppy and though I love it, everyone wants me safe. I hear Mom say, "This way, they can still see each other and feel like they are together," though I will miss Kylie's chin resting on me.

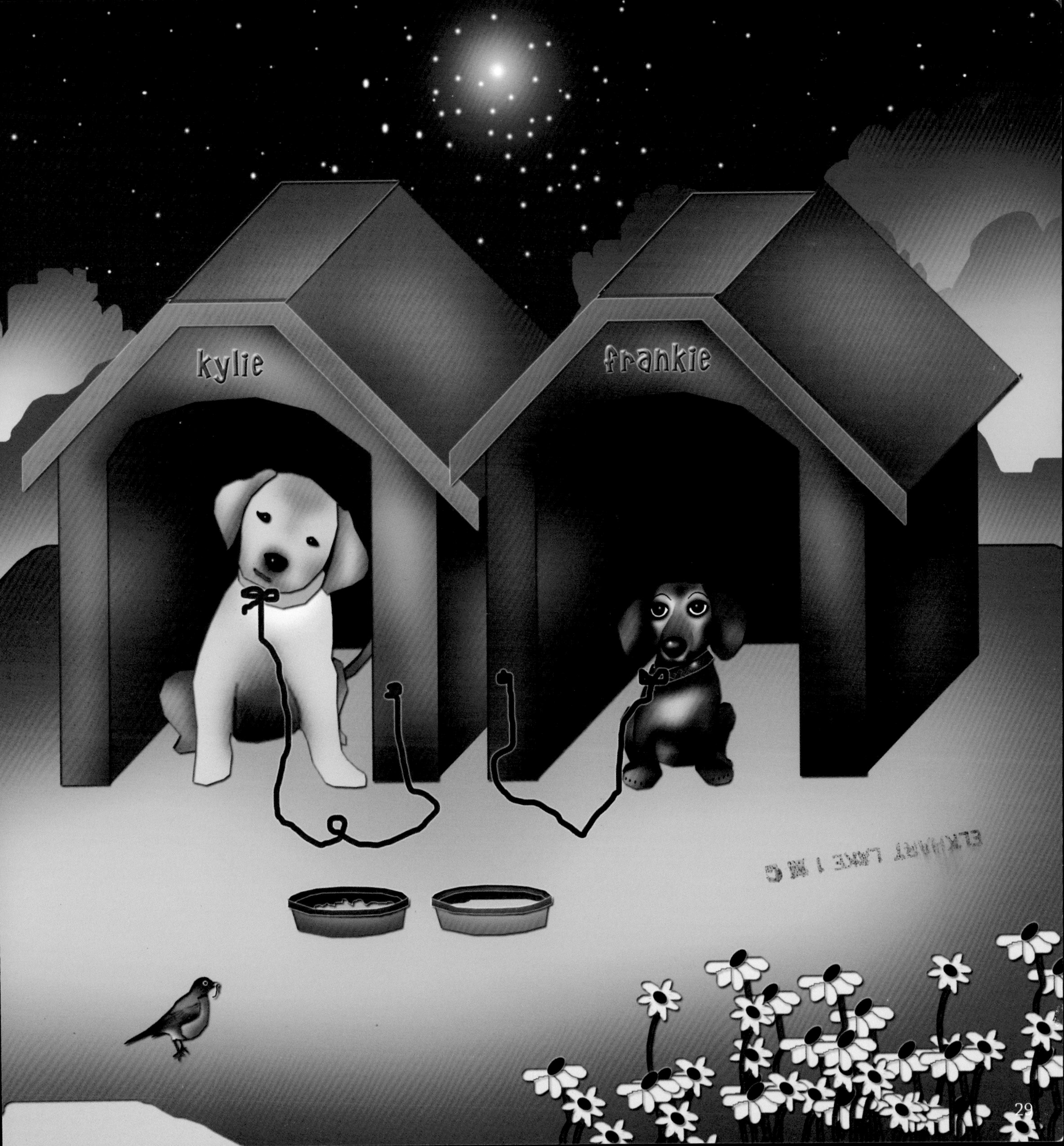
kylie
frankie

Yvonne, the caring lady at the kennel, checks on us often during the day. On Sunday, she feeds us our lunch and says, "I'll be back in an hour to let you outside to play." I simply cannot wait and start to romp about in my kennel. I jump up onto my container of food, but it tips over and I fall hard onto the cement. I feel sharp swords pierce my back. Then I lose feeling in my back legs. When Yvonne comes an hour later, I am not moving. I tilt my head to the side, looking into Yvonne's eyes but do not move an inch. She realizes something is very wrong with me. She starts crying and calls my Aunt Lori right away.

Lori comes and takes me to the local veterinarian's office. The vet tells Lori I am in bad shape. I need surgery right away. I tremble and want Mom, Dad and Kylie to be with me. But I have to be brave by myself.

On the way to the animal hospital, I lie on the passenger side of Lori's car, on my kitty pillow. Lori calls my mom to tell her the news. I hear Lori say, "Don't worry, I'll take good care of Frankie." She then holds the phone to my ear and Mom says, "I love you so much, sweetie. Papa and I will be home soon to be with you." It makes me feel better to hear Mom's soothing voice.

Before going into the hospital, Lori carefully wraps me in a toasty blanket, which comforts me. I am so nervous, I poop on the floor. Lori looks to the older couple sitting in the waiting room and says, "Did Frankie just do that?" They smile and nod their heads. Then the nurse comes out and gently whisks me to the exam room.

The bright lights make me afraid. The vet examines my back and says, "Ruptured disk." She calls my mom and tells her I have a 30% chance of walking again if I go into surgery as soon as possible. I hear her tell Mom, "These little gals are strong. If she does not walk again, she will still lead a happy life."

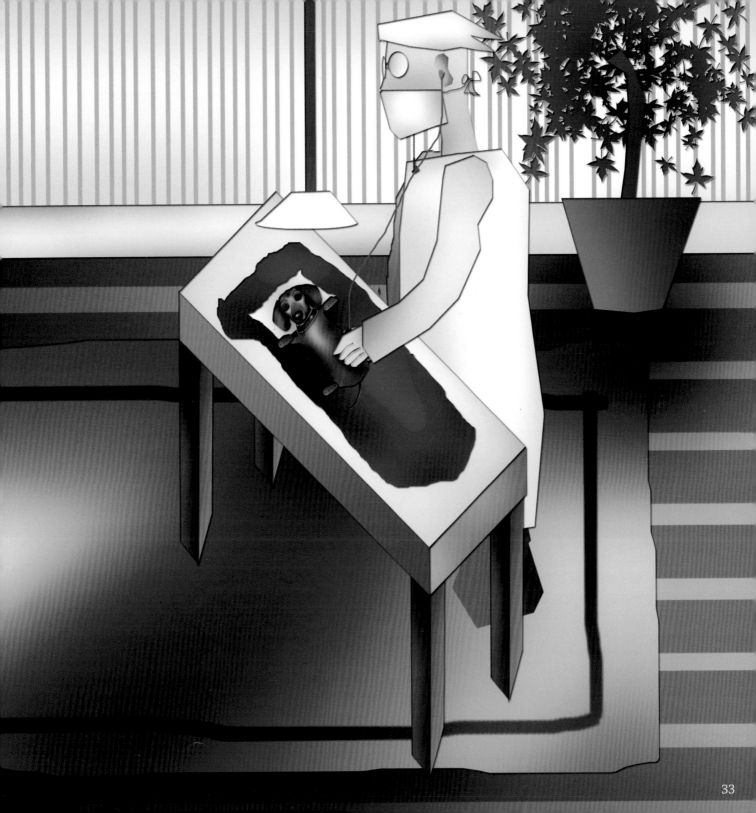

A few moments later, a tiny oxygen mask covers my snout and I drift off to sleep. During surgery, I fall into a deep slumber and dream of warm sunny days, riding in my basket on Mom's bike.

I spend two days at the animal hospital, sleeping, dreaming and believing it will be okay. On the third day, I am brought to a room where I see my mom! Yip-Yip-Hooray! She and my dad skee-daddled back home when they heard I was hurt. It feels warm and safe to be in my mom's loving arms. Mom gives me tons of kisses on the cheek and hugs me so much. I think I will pop!

The next eight weeks, I begin my recovery. I have medicine to take. The pills make me feel better. I also have to stay in my crate for eight weeks and am not allowed to chase after bunnies, play with my toys or cuddle with Kylie. This is hard. But Mom and Dad set my crate in the kitchen. I watch Mom cook dinner, while Dad plays ball with Kylie. Every night, Mom and Dad say, "We love you Frankie. You're looking better and better every day."

Before my accident, I sometimes slept snug in bed next to Dad. After the accident, I sleep in a crate in the bedroom. Mom makes my bed soft and warm with lots of blankets and toys. I learn to sleep by myself and not be scared.

As soon as I can travel, Mom takes me to a specialist in the big city. Trucks rumble by and I bark at the tall buildings in the sky. I feel small. The specialist teaches Mom how to do physical therapy for me.

Pewaukee
Veterinary Service

For the next three months, Mom spends hours helping my muscles grow strong. She moves my legs up and down and in big circles. Then she holds my legs and makes me pretend like I am riding a bicycle. This is my favorite exercise, because it reminds me of being on Mom's bike with her. It feels so good to have blood pumping through my legs. Sometimes by accident, I toot during therapy and Mom grins from ear to ear.

Pool time is another part of my therapy and I have to try and swim in our bathtub. I have an awesome bright orange vest to keep me afloat in the tub as Mom moves my back legs in a swimming motion. After all my hard work, Mom gives me a massage. When she massages me, I close my eyes and feel so loved. We have grown closer.

Everyone hopes I will walk again and I do not want to disappoint them. However, after three months, not much has changed in my legs. But Mom and Dad do not give up on me and find another way for me to walk with wheels! It is a cart made especially for dogs similar to a wheelchair they make for people.

My mom researches the internet and finds a good cart. The president of the company is a dog who looks just like me and her name is Daisy. She is also paralyzed and has a cart. One night Mom and Dad measure from the bottom of the floor to the top of my belly, the base of my neck to the tip of my tail, and then around my little chest. The cart will fit me perfectly and I will be able to zoom down the block!

Three weeks later, a man in a brown truck delivers a package. Out of the wrapping pops my customized cart. My mom cries. I look at her sadly, but she says, "These are happy tears, Frankie!"

The big moment arrives. Mom takes me outside in my cart and says, "Run free, Frankie! I know you can do it!" She has high hopes I will run right away. It is not that easy. I tend to be a little stubborn. I just stand there, waiting for something to happen. I am not sure I want to learn something new. So, in order to get me to try out my new wheels, Mom coaxes me with doggie biscuits. Inch by inch, I move forward. Pretty soon, I am walking around the block and don't even notice the wheels behind me. As we walk by Travis, the neighbor boy, he yells, "Hey, look! That dog has tires!" I hold my head high and roll along with pride.

The fun-filled days of summer are here again which means Saturday mornings at the Farmer's Market. I know Mom is worried about taking me to the market, because the night before, I overhear her telling Dad, "I hope no one will make fun of Frankie." She packs my cart into the back basket and I ride in the front basket. I can see she is nervous because her knuckles are turning white from squeezing the handlebars so tight. So I lick her hand to let her know everything will be fine. We are off! It feels so good to have my ears blow in the breeze again and I can't wait to see my friends at the market. Mom parks our bike and puts me in my cart. Time to show everyone my tires!

One by one, my friends say, "Hey, Frankie, nice to see you!" As Mom walks with me, everyone gathers around and asks what happened to me. Mom explains to them about my back injury and my amazing recovery. I strut my stuff and twirl around in my cart to show them I am going on with my life just like I did before I hurt my legs. I can do anything! We make many new friends and everyone loves me in spite of my tires.

Six months after my accident, I start to use my back legs again. I love to eat my kibble every morning and night and start to stand while I eat. Then I begin trying to walk. I wobble, wobble, wobble like a duck, but I am trying very hard. I still do not have any feeling in my back legs. I am determined to do my best, and whenever I accomplish something new, the pride in Mom and Dad's eyes lets me know they love me.

During the winter, two cats named Sunshine and Shadow come to live with us for three months. I fall in love with Sunshine and think he is handsome. As Sunshine prances around the living room, I use all my might and hop after him. Sunshine jumps on to the sofa and I follow right along. Nothing stops me from being near him. My mom says Sunshine is the reason I try to walk so much now. I think she is right.

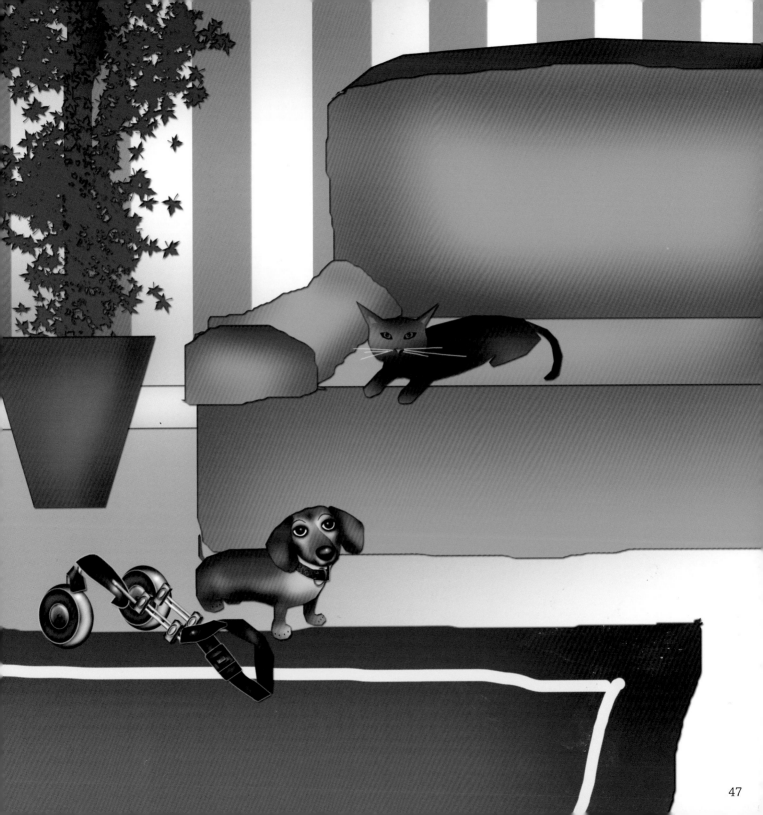

One year has passed since my accident. I still need my tires to play outside, go to the farmer's market and go on walks. But I do not mind at all. I am moving and walking better than anyone ever thought I would. My tires help me to go anywhere I want to go. In the yard, I chase after butterflies and bees. Every afternoon, I squeal out to the end of the driveway and greet the mailman with a loud bark. Each evening, I go on quiet walks in the woods with Mom and Dad. I even take naps on my dancing kitty pillow while in my tires. There is nothing I cannot do. I will always keep on rolling and putting my best paw forward!

# acknowledgements

My journey into the writing world may have never come to light if not for my special Chocolate Lab, Cassie. Without her, I would not be where I am today. Her diagnoses of terminal cancer made me pause long enough to re-evaluate my life. From that soul-searching adventure, I pursued writing a monthly column which led me to writing this, my first children's book. Cassie continues to be with me in spirit, and is a constant guide in my heart. Thank you, my sweet brown dog for teaching me what really matters in life.

This book would not be if it were not for you Frankie, my little dog with the huge heart and amazing attitude. You are unequivocally the biggest inspiration to me, and you continue to amaze me. You are one of the biggest blessings in my life, and I am honored God has entrusted me to care for you.

To my husband, John; without you, I could not be me. For all the times I talked about this book, my challenges, my joys, my ups, my downs, you were there. Your love and devotion for me and our furry family is my most treasured gift.

I would not be the woman I am today without my mom, my best friend, my confidant, my soul sister. Your unwavering support as I wrote and re-wrote this book, sustained me again and again and again. Your faith in me is a gift I hold close to my heart, and it inspires me to be the best that I can be.

To my friend, Diane Krause-Stetson (www.leadyourlife.com); you were the first to plant the seed of a children's book in my mind. Through your authentic coaching style you helped me to see what really matters in this thing called life. You brought the true me into the open, and your endless support catapulted me forward when I felt stuck. You are one special lady.

To Linda Verville, author of For Pete's Sake (www.readforpetessake.com). I believe everything happens for a reason, and our friendship was meant to be. I am grateful for all your gracious, enthusiastic help and for enduring my endless email of questions. Your generosity is a beautiful thing. I'm glad I found you.

A sincere and warm thank you to my sister-in-law, Lori Smith, for your utmost care and love for Frankie during the first critical hours, as well as your continued support as Frankie recovered. You're the best auntie a dog could ever hope for.

To my illustrator, Victoria Kay Lieffring, thank you for bringing my words to life with your amazing illustrations. You are extremely gifted and talented.

Everyone who writes needs a support system of encouragement, and I am grateful to be part of the Women's Writing Circle. Each of you contributed to my growth, and went above and beyond with your feedback. Your enthusiasm for this book is a gift for which I will always be thankful.

To all the veterinarians, technicians, and staff at Kettle Moraine Veterinary Center. You go beyond the call of duty and I feel fortunate to have you care for my animals. Your exuberance for my book has touched me deeply.

To the veterinarians and technicians of Appleton Animal Referral Hospital for your expertise and knowledge in putting Frankie back together again. What a remarkable clinic!

"To my family and friends and your enthusiastic questions of, "How's your book coming?" and "When can I buy your book?" Thank you for your sweet, kind support. I am grateful."

Barbara wrote "Frankie, The Walk 'N Roll Dog" to give hope and inspiration to all who face challenges. Her lifetime love of animals lead her to realize that Frankie's paralysis was an opportunity to spread a positive message. Barbara receives constant compassionate reactions when she is out with Frankie in her local town. People are fascinated by the little dog with tires, frequently asking her what happened to Frankie. The warmth, kindness and encouragement from strangers, as well as family and friends, lead Barbara to writing this, her first children's book.

Since 2005 Barbara's column, "For the Love of Animals" has appeared in the Depot Dispatch. Her column shares stories of the daily antics and lives of her four-legged companions as well as other furry friends she has met.

Barbara shares her quaint "cottage in the city" in Elkhart Lake, Wisconsin with her loving husband John and her sweet critters. Fur abounds on the kitchen hardwood floor on a daily basis from Kylie, a yellow English Labrador, Frankie, a miniature dachshund and Dani, a tabby striped cat.

Barbara hopes Frankie's story will help anyone facing a challenge to realize they always have a choice as to how they will overcome a challenge and that hope is all you need to move forward.

You can read more about Barbara on her website at, www.joyfulpaws.com

"My little dog—a heartbeat at my feet."
-Edith Wharton